"Have you got the coconuts?" Sunil asks Meena as they put on their coats.

They are all wearing warm coats as the evening air is cold.

Meena looks in the bag. "Yes. They are with the sweets."

"Have you got your knife in your pocket?" Sunil asks his father.

"Oh, yes. I wouldn't forget that tonight."

They leave the flat, and walk down the road
to the park, the children almost running.
  "Look! I can see the fire," Sunil calls back.

They can see the red glow and smoke
billowing in the dark sky.

As they reach the park they join others who are moving round the fire.

"Here. Give me the coconuts," Father tells Meena.

He takes them and rolls them into the red, glowing fire, pushing them further in with a stick.

"Now, you keep your eye on them Sunil. In a few minutes we will be able to eat them."

Grandad stands with Sunil, his face glowing in the heat.

Meena is helping her mother who has brought a tray with lamps and flowers which she lays on the ground. She lights some joss sticks, and pushes them into the ground. Meena thinks they smell lovely.

Then her mother says prayers as she lights the lamp. Meena kneels beside her trying to stop people from treading on the tray as they pass.

"I think the coconuts will be ready now,"
Grandad cries.

Father rolls them out of the fire with a stick,
but they are too hot to touch.

When they are cooler Father cracks them, and cuts the warm coconut.

"I like this," Sunil tries to say, chewing at the same time.

"Here. Share this around," his father tells him, putting another piece in his hand.

Sunil walks around asking other people if they would like some coconut.

Everyone is happy, talking, laughing, running away when the wind blows the smoke into their eyes.

All too soon Father calls "Come on now. Time to go home. We will have more fun tomorrow with the Holi Game."

"Oo. Good," thinks Sunil.

The next day the children are very excited. They cannot wait until it is time to leave home. They put on their old cotton clothes, and fill squeezy bottles with red coloured water. They hurry to the big hall where the Holi Game is to be played.

Soon they are joining in the fun. There is such a lot of noise and laughter as everyone joins in.

Some are throwing coloured powder from plates, and others are squeezing bottles so that the red water shoots out in a spray.

"Got you!" screams Sunil as he creeps up behind Meena. They do look a mess!

Later, when they are eating sweets, Father tells them, "We play that game because the god Krishna used to play tricks on people."

Special words in this book

Holi   Hindu Spring festival of colour
joss sticks scented sticks lit for their perfume